This book belongs to

....

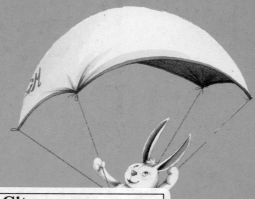

Quarto is the authority on a wide range of topics.

Quarto educates, entertains and enriches the lives of our readers—enthusiasts and lovers of hands-on living.

www.quartoknows.com

© 2018 Quarto Publishing plc

First published in 2018 by QED Publishing, an imprint of The Quarto Group. The Old Brewery, 6 Blundell Street, London N7 9BH, United Kingdom. T (0)20 7700 6700 F (0)20 7700 8066 www.QuartoKnows.com

A catalogue record for this book is available from the British Library.

ISBN 978-1-91241-378-2

Based on the original story by Malachy Doyle and Gill McLean
Author of adapted text: Katie Woolley
Series Editor: Joyce Bentley
Series Designer: Sarah Peden

Manufactured in Dongguan, China TL042018

9 8 7 6 5 4 3 2 1

MIX
Paper from responsible sources
FSC® C104723

**Reading
Gems**

Three,
Two,
One...

The toys wanted to go into space.

Chick

Elephant

Horse

Sheep

Pig

Dog

Lion

Monkey

Giraffe

Rabbit

But Giraffe was too tall.

I am too tall.

10...

Elephant was too big.

The rocket was very dark.

Sheep did not like the dark.

I do not want to go.

Chick was too small.

Space is too big for me. I am too small.

7...

Monkey, Rabbit and Lion still wanted to go.

But Lion did not like heights.

6...

15

And Pig did not like heights.

5...

Horse was too tired.

I am tired.

4...

19

Dog and Monkey did not
want to meet a space man.

But Rabbit still wanted to go into space.

1...

Blast off!

Story Words

blast off!

Chick

dark

Dog

Elephant

Giraffe

Horse

Lion

Monkey

Pig

Rabbit

rocket

Sheep

space man

toys

Let's Talk About Three, Two, One...

Look carefully at the book cover.

How many toy animals can you count?

Can you name the animals too?

In the story, the animals are deciding who gets to go into space.

Would you like to go into space?

What things might you see in space?

The story is all about counting from 10 to 1.

Can you count backwards from 10?

What sound do you think the rocket makes when it blasts off into space?

How do you think each animal feels when he or she realises they won't be going into space?

Look back at the pictures and discuss the reasons why each animal could not go into space.

Did you like the story?

Who was your favourite character?

Are you glad that Rabbit was the one who went into space?

Fun and Games

Look at the toys below. Which one begins with the letter 'r'?

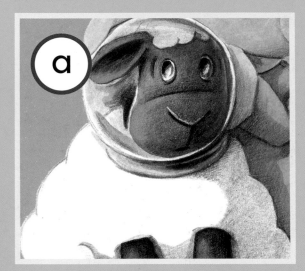

Sheep

Lion

Rabbit

Pig

Can you put these animals in size order, from smallest to tallest?

Giraffe

Elephant

Horse

Lion

Rabbit

Pig

Sheep

Chick

Your Turn

Now that you have read the story,
have a go at telling it in your own words.
Use the pictures below to help you.

31

GET TO KNOW READING GEMS

Reading Gems is a series of books that has been written for children who are learning to read. The books have been created in consultation with a literacy specialist.

The books fit into four levels, with each level getting more challenging as a child's confidence and reading ability grows. The simple text and fun illustrations provide gradual, structured practice of reading. Most importantly, these books are good stories that are fun to read!

Level 1 is for children who are taking their first steps into reading. Story themes and subjects are familiar to young children, and there is lots of repetition to build reading confidence.

Level 2 is for children who have taken their first reading steps and are becoming readers. Story themes are still familiar but sentences are a bit longer, as children begin to tackle more challenging vocabulary.

Level 3 is for children who are developing as readers. Stories and subjects are varied, and more descriptive words are introduced.

Level 4 is for readers who are rapidly growing in reading confidence and independence. There is less repetition on the page, broader themes are explored and plot lines straddle multiple pages.

Three, Two, One... is all about a group of toys wanting a space adventure. It explores themes of courage, counting and space.

Level 1